doodle
shapes

Buster Books

Start at point 1 and join the dots to draw these snails' slimy trails.

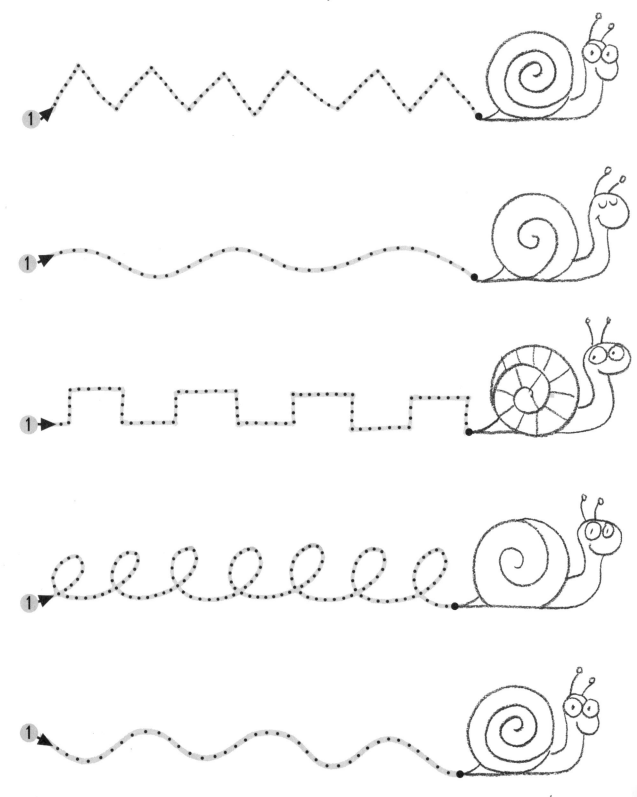

Start at point **1** and join the dots to complete
the toys in the window.

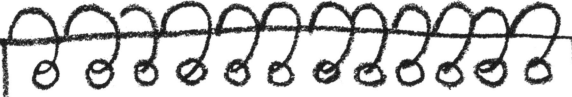

Start at point ① and join the dots to finish the square.

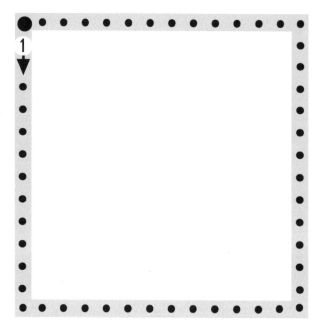

Start at point ① and join the dots to finish the circle.

Start at point **1** and join the dots to finish the triangle.

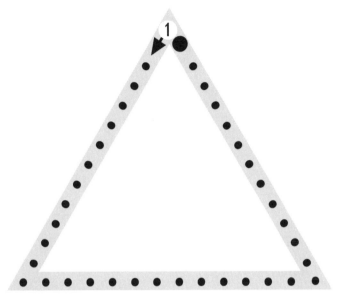

Start at point **1** and join the dots to finish the rectangle.

Start at point ① and join the dots to finish the square.

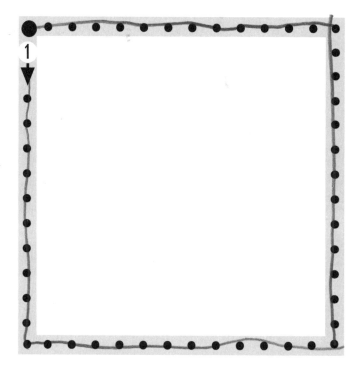

Join the dots to write the word.

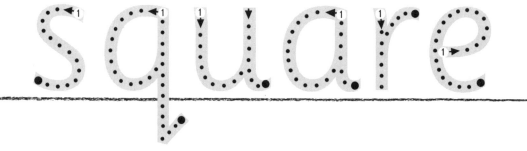

Complete the pretty presents.

Start at point ① and join the dots to finish the circle.

Join the dots to write the word.

circle

Complete the circles to cover the pizza in pepperoni.

Start at point 1 and join the dots to finish the triangle.

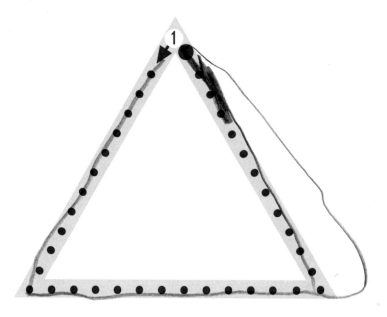

Join the dots to write the word.

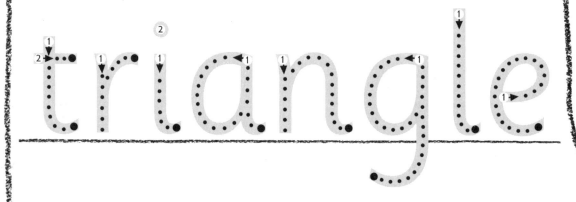

Finish the tents in the campsite.

Start at point **1** and join the dots to finish the rectangle.

Join the dots to write the word.

rectangle

Complete the frames around the pictures.

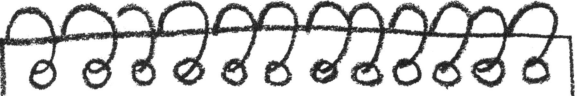

Start at point ① and join the dots to finish the square.

Join the dots to finish the squares,
then draw a square of your own.

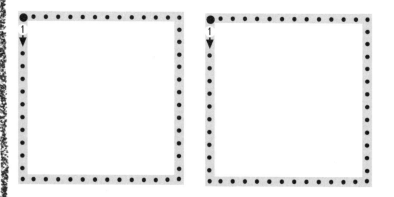

Complete the squares in this picture.

Can you draw more windows?

Start at point **1** and join the dots to finish the circle.

Join the dots to finish the circles,
then draw a circle of your own.

Complete the circles in this picture.

Can you draw
more bubbles?

Start at point ①and join the dots to finish the triangle.

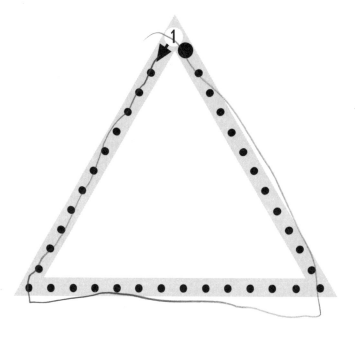

Join the dots to finish the triangles,
then draw a triangle of your own.

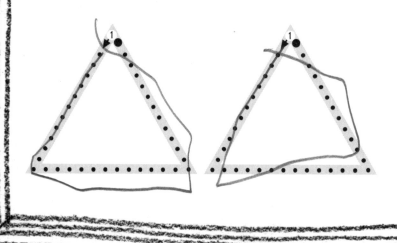

Complete the triangles in this picture.

Can you draw more sails?

Start at point ① and join the dots to finish the rectangle.

Join the dots to finish the rectangles,
then draw a rectangle of your own.

Complete the rectangles in this picture.

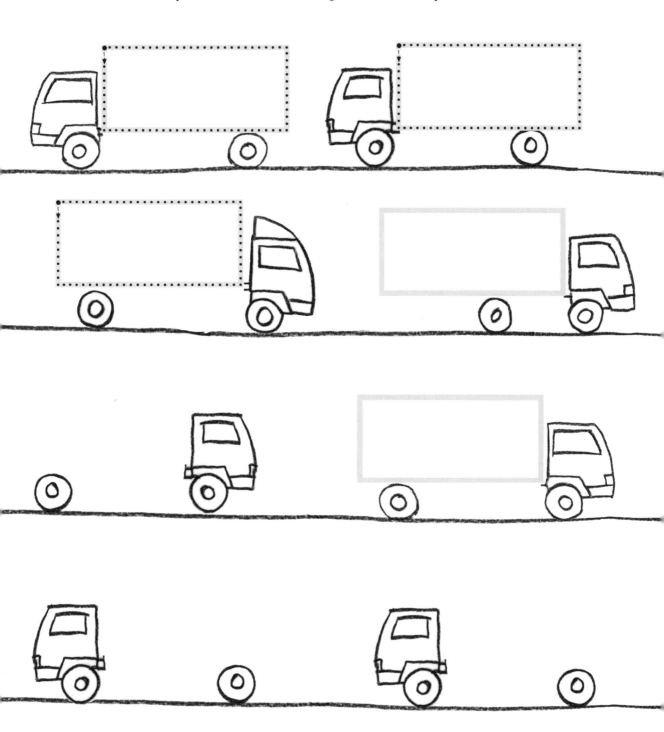

Can you draw more trucks?

There are five squares in this picture.
Can you spot them all? Doodle some passengers
in the windows of the bus.

There are two squares in this picture.
Colour them red.

There are ten circles in this picture.
Can you count all the balls and decorate them?

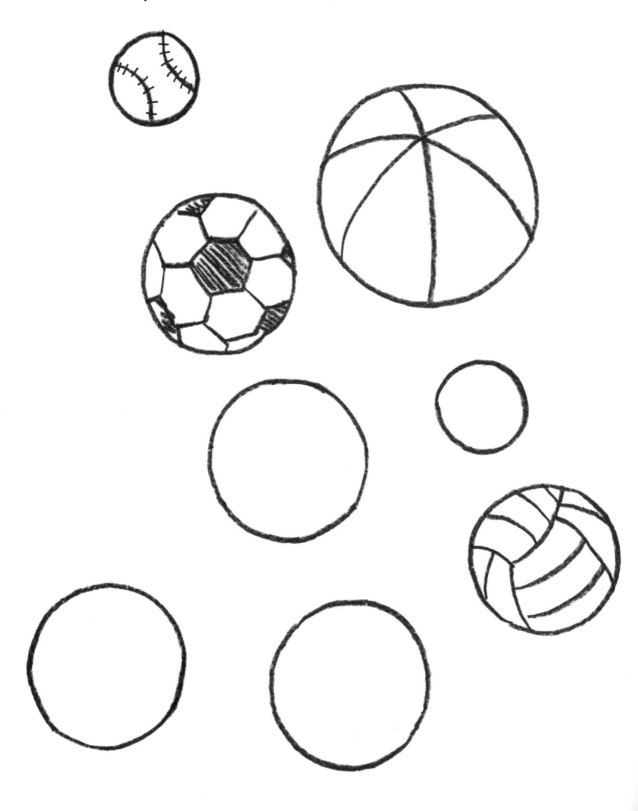

There are four circles in this picture.
Colour them yellow.

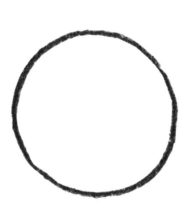

There are five triangles in this picture. Can you see them all? Make the king's beard very long and curly.

There are eight triangles in this picture.
Colour them green.

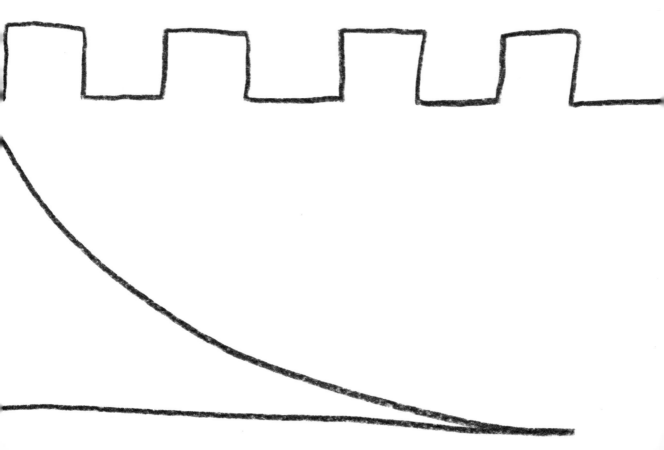

There are four rectangles in this picture. Can you spot them all and draw smoke coming out of the train's funnel?

There are six rectangles in this picture.
Colour them brown.

Start at point 1 and join the dots to finish the heart.

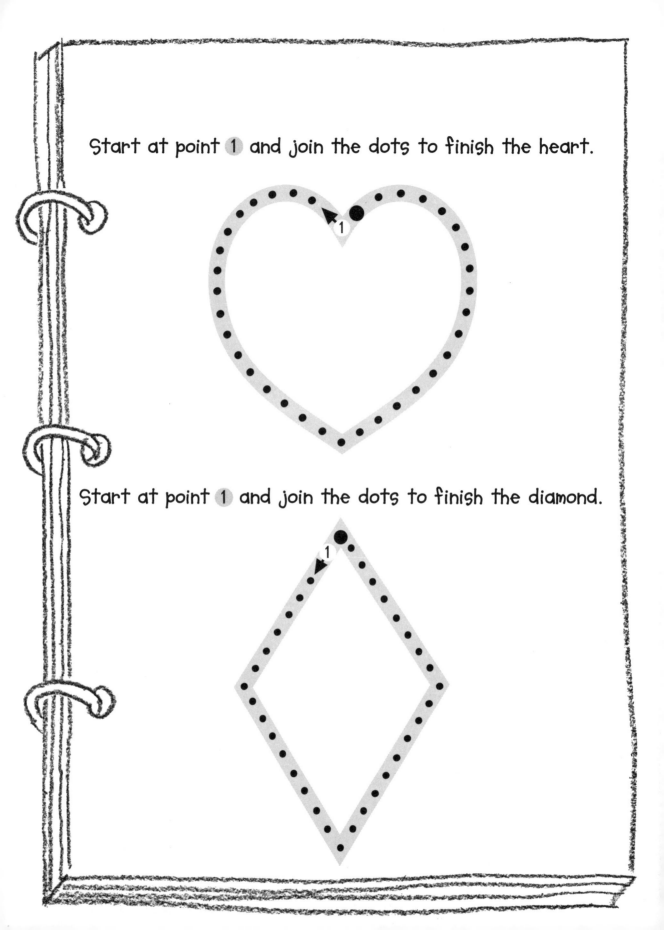

Start at point 1 and join the dots to finish the diamond.

Start at point ① and join the dots to finish the star.

Start at point ① and join the dots to finish the oval.

Start at point ①and join the dots to finish the heart.

Join the dots to write the word.

Finish the beautiful butterflies.

Start at point ① and join the dots to finish the diamond.

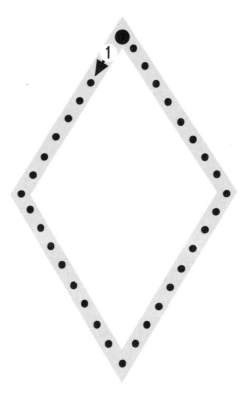

Join the dots to write the word.

Finish the kites.

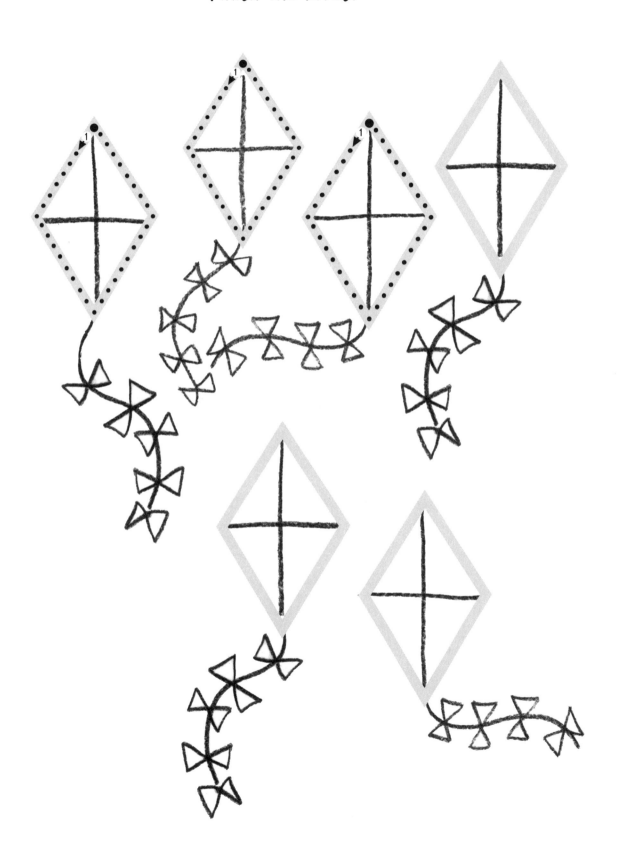

Start at point ① and join the dots to finish the star.

Join the dots to write the word.

Complete the stars in this circus scene.

Start at point **1** and join the dots to finish the oval.

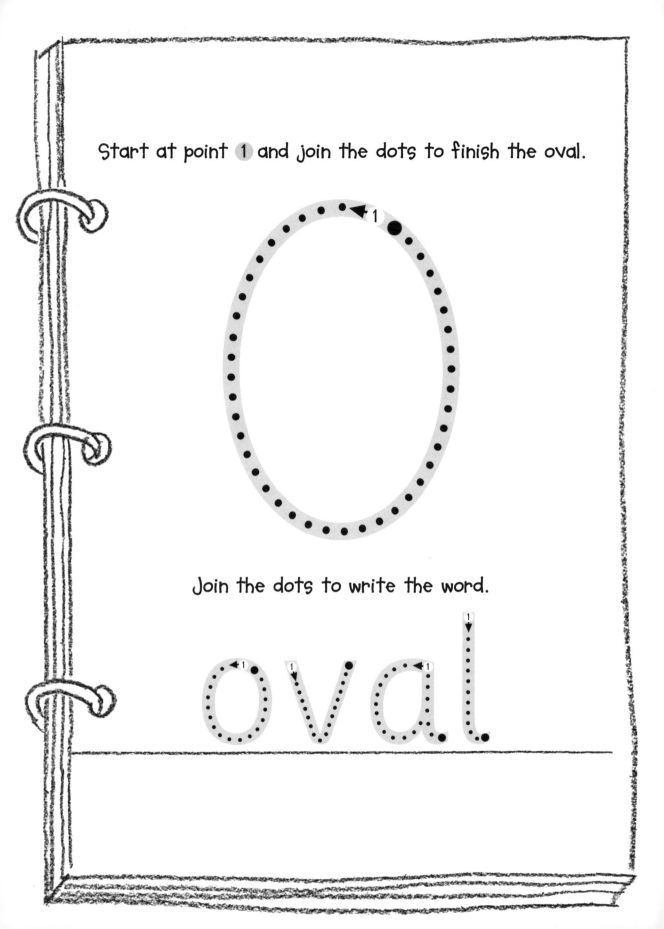

Join the dots to write the word.

oval

Fill the nest with eggs.

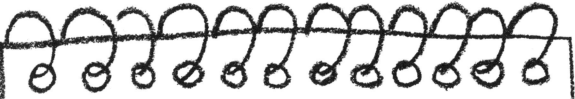

Start at point **1** and join the dots to finish the heart.

Join the dots to finish the hearts,
then draw a heart of your own.

Complete the heart-shaped leaves and draw some more?

Start at point ① and join the dots to finish the diamond.

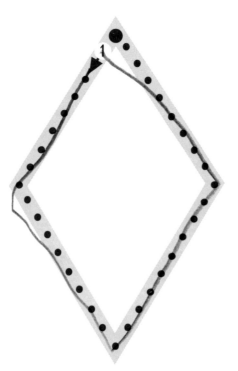

Join the dots to finish the diamonds,
then draw a diamond of your own.

Complete the diamond shapes on
the snake. Then add more diamonds
to finish its markings.

Start at point ① and join the dots to finish the star.

Join the dots to finish the stars,
then draw a star of your own.

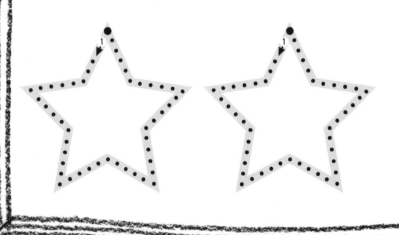

Complete the stars in this picture.
Can you draw more stars?

Start at point ① and join the dots to finish the oval.

1

Join the dots to finish the ovals,
then draw an oval of your own.

1

1

Complete the ovals in this picture.
Can you draw more turtles?

There are six hearts in this picture. Can you count them all, then decorate the queen's dress?

There are four hearts in this picture.
Colour them orange.

There are eight diamonds in this picture. Point to them all.
Can you draw a big sun to dry the washing?

There are six diamond-shaped jewels in this picture.
Colour them pink.

There are seven stars in this picture.
Find them, then fill the sea with fish.

There are nine stars in this picture.
Colour them yellow.

There are six ovals in this picture.
Find them all, then add more grain for the chicks to eat.

There are two ovals in this picture.
Colour them red.

BIGGER AND SMALLER

Look at this box.   This box is bigger.   This box is smaller.

Look at this cookie.   Draw a cookie   Draw one
                       that is bigger.   that is smaller.

THICKER AND THINNER

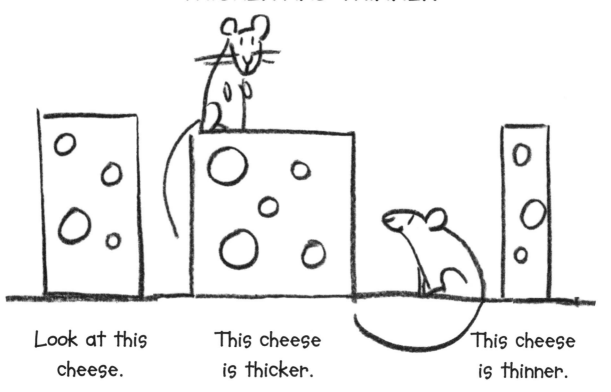

Look at this
cheese.

This cheese
is thicker.

This cheese
is thinner.

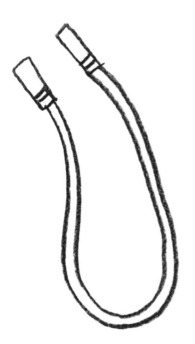

Look at this rope.

Draw a rope
that is thicker.

Draw a rope
that is thinner.

TALLER AND SHORTER

Look at this giraffe.

This giraffe is taller.

This giraffe is shorter.

Look at this tree.

Draw a tree that is taller.

Draw a tree that is shorter.

LONGER AND SHORTER

 Look at this carrot.

 This carrot
is longer.

 This carrot
is shorter.

 Look at this pencil.

Draw a pencil
that is longer.

Draw a pencil
that is shorter.

Complete the picture with shapes of all sizes.

3.5m

5

GROCERY

Complete the picture with shapes of all sizes.

PET

SHOW ♡

How to get in shape ...

Read the instructions in this book with your child. The pages at the front will help them to practise holding and using a pencil, before tackling the shapes on the following pages. First, they will learn to form a shape by tracing the dots provided. Then they can test their skills by incorporating the shapes into scenes. Writing the names of the shapes will help to consolidate their knowledge. Learning how to form shapes has never been more fun!

Get a grip!

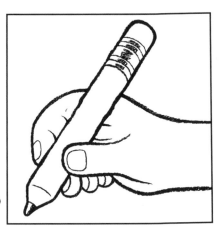

A pencil should be held between a child's thumb and forefinger and supported by the middle finger. This is known as a 'tripod grip'. It can be tricky for a child to achieve at first. Encourage them, but don't worry too much if they find it difficult. Using triangular or chunky pens or pencils can make it easier for a child to master the the basics of writing and drawing.

Don't get 'left' behind

Left-handers needn't feel left out. If you are left-handed and your child is right-handed, use your right hand when showing your child how to hold a pencil and write. If your child is left-handed, use your left hand.

Written by Sally Pilkington
Illustrated by Nancy Meyers
Designed by Zoe Quayle

First published in Great Britain in 2011 by Buster Books, an imprint of Michael O'Mara Books Limited, 9 Lion Yard, Tremadoc Road, London SW4 7NQ

Text copyright © Buster Books 2011
Illustrations copyright © Nancy Meyers 2011

ISBN: 978-1-907151-47-7

2 4 6 8 10 9 7 5 3 1
www.mombooks.com/busterbooks

This book was printed in February 2011 at L.E.G.O., Viale dell'Industria 2, 36100, Vicenza, Italy.